big
NATE
WELCOME TO
MY WORLD

More

big
NATE

adventures from

LINCOLN PEIRCE

---

big NATE
WELCOME TO MY WORLD

by LINCOLN PEIRCE

SCHOLASTIC INC.

THERE'S MY SCHOOL: P.S. 38.

LOOKS LIKE A SCHOOL, ALL RIGHT!

I THINK IT LOOKS **WONDER-FUL!**

I CAN'T WAIT TO SEE YOUR CLASSROOMS AND MEET ALL YOUR TEACHERS! THIS IS SO **EXCITING!**

IT IS?

WE DON'T GET OUT MUCH.

QUIET, VERN.

BEFORE HOMEROOM, I HAVE TO STOP BY MY LOCKER.

FAIR ENOUGH!

ALL THE SIXTH GRADE LOCKERS ARE ALONG THIS WALL.

OOH! WHICH ONE'S YOURS?

NEVER MIND.

STAND BACK.

YOU'RE TWENTY SECONDS LATE. THAT MEANS DETENTION.

WAIT! I MEAN, YES, I WAS LATE, BUT...

I WAS SHOWING MY GRAND-PARENTS AROUND, AND...

THAT'S HARDLY AN EXCUSE.

YOUR CLASSMATES ARE ALL HOSTING **THEIR** GRANDPARENTS, AND **THEY** SOMEHOW MADE IT TO CLASS ON TIME.

THE GREAT

Peirce

WHAT A...

QUIET, VERN.

WELCOME TO MY WORLD.

ALL RIGHT, CLASS, OPEN YOUR TEXT-BOOKS TO PAGE...

HOLD IT, **HOLD** IT!

IT'S **GRANDPARENTS DAY!** HOW COME WE'RE DOING THE USUAL STUFF? CAN'T WE DO SOMETHING **SPECIAL**, LIKE PLAY A GAME OR WATCH A MOVIE?

I HAVE TOO MUCH RESPECT FOR ALL THE GRANDPARENTS TO CONCOCT SOME SORT OF PHONY ACTIVITY TO MAKE THE CLASS MORE "ENTERTAINING."

SHE'S GOOD.

PERSONALLY, I'D **WELCOME** A PHONY ACTIVITY RIGHT ABOUT NOW.

Peirce

THAT'S MY GRAND-FATHER OVER THERE! HE'S A WELL-KNOWN **DOCTOR!**

HM. VERY INTERESTING, GINA.

HE'S CHIEF OF SURGERY AT THE BEST HOSPITAL IN THE STATE! HE'S WON ALL SORTS OF AWARDS! HE'S BEEN ON TELEVISION!

BET MY GRANDFATHER COULD TAKE HIM.

THINK YOU COULD TAKE THAT GUY, GRAMPS?

OH YEAH. IN MY SLEEP.

THAT'S GINA'S GRAND-FATHER OVER THERE, AND SEE THAT LADY NEXT TO HIM? THAT'S HIS **WIFE!**

SHE MUST BE, LIKE, FORTY YEARS YOUNGER THAN HE IS!

YES, AT **LEAST!** THAT'S... THAT'S...

THAT'S VERY, VERY, VERY, VERY, VERY, VERY, VERY, VERY, VERY, VERY, VERY, VERY WRONG.

Peirce

I LOVE ALL YOUR ART PROJECTS, SWEETIE!

WE DIDN'T EVEN **HAVE** ART WHEN I WAS IN SCHOOL!

WE HAD **WOOD SHOP** WITH MR. MULCAHEY! HE HAD NO **CLUE** WHAT HE WAS DOING! ALL THE TOOLS WERE IN **HORRIBLE** CONDITION!

I CAN'T TELL YOU HOW MANY TIMES I WAS ALMOST **KILLED** IN THAT CLASS!

VERN...

REALLY?

WANT TO SEE A NASTY SCAR?

VERN...

GUYS!

NATE! HALLO!

OH, HEY, ARTUR.

GRAM, THIS IS ARTUR.

HELLO! VERY NICE TO MEETING YOU!

YOU ARE ENJOY GRANDPARENTS DAY?

OH, YES! VERY MUCH!

DID YOU BRING **YOUR** GRANDPARENTS TODAY, ARTUR?

NO. THEY ARE LIVE VERY FAR AWAY.

...SO THERE IS NOBODY FOR ME TO SHOWING AROUND.

WELL, **THAT** DOESN'T SEEM FAIR!

WHAT ABOUT IF I SHOW **YOU** AROUND?

WHY, I'D BE **DELIGHTED**!

ARTUR JUST HIJACKED MY GRANDMA.

I'M OKAY WITH IT, AS LONG AS SHE'S BACK BY SUPPERTIME.

?

HOW COME THERE ARE SO MANY MORE GRAND**MOTHERS** HERE THAN GRAND**FATHERS**?

BECAUSE MEN DIE EARLIER.

WE MATURE LATER, AND WE DIE EARLIER.

AND IN BETWEEN, ALL YOU DO IS WATCH FOOTBALL.

HE LIKES THE SIDE-LINE REPORT-ERS.

...AND **CROSS-WORD** PUZZLES! LET'S NOT FORGET THE **CROSSWORD** PUZZLES!

IS IT REALLY TRUE THAT WOMEN LIVE LONGER THAN MEN, GRAMPS?

IT'S A STONE COLD FACT.

BUT **WHY**? WHY DO MEN DIE YOUNGER?

VERN, I NEED TO VISIT THE RESTROOM. HOLD MY PURSE.

THERE ARE JUST CERTAIN THINGS THAT AGE YOU.

THIS IS MR. STAPLES, MY MATH TEACHER!

OH, MATH WAS MY **FAVORITE** IN HIGH SCHOOL!

UNFORTUNATELY, IT WAS DIFFICULT FOR A YOUNG WOMAN TO HAVE A CAREER IN MATH BACK THEN.

SO INSTEAD... ☆SIGH☆... I GOT MARRIED.

I COULD HAVE DONE WITHOUT THE SIGH, MARGE.

OH, VERN! I WAS **SWOONING!**

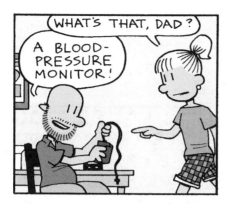

DAD, THAT LUNCH YOU PACKED FOR ME TODAY WAS **BRUTAL.**

YOU'RE WELCOME.

IF YOU DIDN'T LIKE IT, WHY DIDN'T YOU TRADE LUNCHES WITH A FRIEND?

I **TRIED** THAT! BUT YOU THINK THAT'S **EASY?**

"HI THERE! WANT TO TRADE YOUR PIZZA AND COOKIES..."

"..FOR A **CELERY STICK** AND A **BEAN SPROUT PITA?"**

DID YOU MENTION THE PITA WAS WHOLE WHEAT?

Peirce

HERE, DAD.

WHAT'S THIS?

A LIST OF MY FAVORITE FOODS! NOW YOU WON'T WASTE YOUR TIME PACKING LUNCHES I WON'T **EAT!**

YOU FORGOT THE COMMA BETWEEN "CHOCOLATE" AND "BURRITOS."

NO, I DIDN'T!

MR. GALVIN, MY DAD KEEPS SENDING ME TO SCHOOL WITH **NASTY** LUNCHES. I HAVEN'T EATEN SINCE BREAKFAST. I'M **STARVING**.

MM-HM.

I DON'T SUPPOSE YOU... ✳'HEH HEH'✳... HAVE ANYTHING EDIBLE IN YOUR DESK?

WELL, LET'S TAKE A LOOK...

I'M NOT SURE A TUBE OF EXTRA-STRENGTH DENTAL ADHESIVE IS GOING TO TAKE THE EDGE OFF.

Peirce

WHAT IS **THAT?**

AN EXPERIMENT, TEDDY. I'M SICK OF THE HORRIBLE LUNCHES MY DAD MAKES FOR ME.

...SO I TOOK EVERYTHING I COULD FIND IN OUR KITCHEN AND THREW IT ALL TOGETHER IN A PLASTIC BOWL.

NARF! SLURPF! SLOSH! NOSH!

MAPLE SYRUP AND RANCH DRESSING DON'T GO TOGETHER.

I'LL WRITE THAT DOWN.

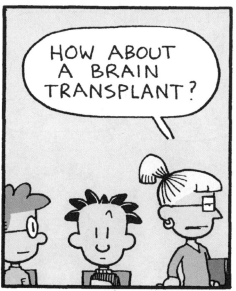

NO MATTER WHAT YOU GET ON THE SOCIAL STUDIES FINAL, NATE, YOU CAN'T GET AN **A** FOR THE SEMESTER.

NUTS. WHAT DO I NEED TO GET A B?

UMMM... A HUNDRED.

A **HUNDRED**? THAT'S A LITTLE HIGH, FRANCIS.

I MEAN, I WANT A GOOD GRADE AND ALL, BUT I DON'T WANT TO PUT TOO MUCH **PRESSURE** ON MYSELF!

THAT'S NEVER REALLY BEEN A PROBLEM FOR YOU.

HOW 'BOUT A NICE, COMFY C MINUS?

NATE, IF YOU GET A HUNDRED ON THE SOCIAL STUDIES FINAL, YOU'LL GET A **B** FOR THE SEMESTER! WHY NOT **TRY**?

BECAUSE...

BECAUSE HE COULDN'T GET A HUNDRED ON AN EXAM IF HIS LIFE **DEPENDED** ON IT.

☆SNORT!☆

WELL, **THAT** WASN'T VERY NICE!

GAME ON.

SO GINA DOESN'T THINK I CAN GET A HUNDRED ON THE SOCIAL STUDIES FINAL, EH? I'LL SHOW **HER**!

BUT YOU CAN'T **STAND** GINA! WHY DO YOU CARE WHAT **SHE** THINKS?

BECAUSE IT **MOTIVATES** ME, FRANCIS!

TOM BRADY HATES THE STEELERS, RIGHT? THAT'S WHY HE WANTS TO **BEAT** THEM SO BAD!

YOU'RE COMPARING YOURSELF TO THE MVP OF THE NFL.

THERE'S NO COMPARISON. I HAVE BETTER HAIR.

YOUR SHO-CALLED **NOTESH** ARE A COMPLETE **JOKE**!

OKAY, SO I'M NOT GREAT AT TAKING NOTES! THERE'S NO NEED TO BE **RUDE**!

YOU KNOW, PETER, MOST FIRST-GRADERS WOULD TREAT A SIXTH-GRADER WITH A LITTLE MORE **RESPECT**!

MOSHT SHIXTH-GRADERSH WOULDN'T ASHK A FIRSHT-GRADER TO BE THEIR TUTOR.

TOUCHÉ.

...WHICH REMINDSH ME, WE SHOULD DISCUSSH MY FEE.

Peirce

OKAY, I'M GOING TO QUIZ YOU. I'LL GIVE YOU AN EVENT, AND YOU TELL ME THE DATE.

PIECE O' CAKE!

GETTYSHBURG ADDRESSH.

JUNE 23RD, 2011!

YOU CAN'T POSSHIBLY BE THISH SHTUPID.

THE 22ND? NO! THE 24TH!

GIVE IT TO ME STRAIGHT, PETER: WHAT ARE MY CHANCES OF GETTING A HUNDRED ON MY SOCIAL STUDIES FINAL?

ROUGHLY THE EQUIV- ALENT OF CUSHTER'SH CHANCESH AT THE LITTLE BIGHORN.

YES!

...RIGHT?

TELL YOU WHAT, LET'SH REVIEW CHAPTER TWELVE.

YOU'RE ON DECK, NATE! GRAB A BAT!

RIGHT, COACH!

CLAP CLAP

WANT A QUICK SCOUTING REPORT ON THE PITCHER?

NO.

WHY NOT?

BECAUSE YOU DRIVE ME **NUTS** WITH ALL YOUR STUPID STATS AND SABERMETRICS, FRANCIS!

WHAT'S **THIS** GUY'S E.R.A. AGAINST PINCH HITTERS ON THURSDAYS? WHAT'S **THAT** GUY'S W.H.I.P. IN ODD-NUMBERED INNINGS? WHO **CARES**?

THAT STUFF MEANS NOTHING IN THE BATTER'S BOX! IF YOU WANT TO GIVE ME A SCOUTING REPORT, MAKE IT INFORMATION I CAN **USE!**

DOOF!

I WAS GOING TO MENTION THAT HE'S A LITTLE WILD.

... JUST LIKE THE SHERMAN ANTITRUST ACT, WHICH PASSED ON JULY 2ND, 1890, MARKING THE BEGINNING OF THE GOVERNMENT'S EFFORT TO RESTRICT MONOPOLIES.

LOOKS LIKE YOU **DIDN'T** GET A HUNDRED ON THE FINAL, EINSTEIN!

A **99**?

MRS. GODFREY, WHY DID I GET A **99** ON THE FINAL? I GOT EVERYTHING **RIGHT**!

YOU DIDN'T WRITE YOUR NAME IN THE SPACE PROVIDED. THAT'S AN AUTOMATIC ONE-POINT DEDUCTION.

OH, HOW I HATE HER.

WANT TO SEE WHAT A **REAL** HUNDRED LOOKS LIKE?

MRS. GODFREY, I NEEDED A HUNDRED ON THE FINAL TO GET A B FOR THE SEMESTER.

UH HUH...

WELL, SINCE I CAME SO CLOSE — Y'KNOW, GETTING A 99 AND EVERYTHING — DO YOU THINK MAYBE YOU COULD GIVE ME A B ANYWAY?

WHY WOULD I DO THAT?

BECAUSE YOU'RE SO STINKIN' NICE!

HAVE A GOOD SUMMER.

I CAN'T BELIEVE MRS. GODFREY GAVE ME A **99** INSTEAD OF A **HUNDRED!** WHAT A **JERK!**

YOU KNOW WHAT I HOPE? I HOPE SHE GOES ON **SAFARI** THIS SUMMER AT SOME SORT OF AFRICAN **GAME PRESERVE!**...

...AND THEN SHE WANDERS OFF ALONE AND GETS **ATTACKED** BY A **CRAZED WILDEBEEST!**

THEN, AS SHE STAGGERS BACK TO THE TOUR BUS, THE HYENAS MOVE IN...

HE GETS VERY CREATIVE WITH HIS REVENGE FANTASIES.

AHHH, **SUMMER**!

HEY! I JUST THOUGHT OF SOMETHING!

WE WERE SO BUSY CRAMMING FOR **FINALS**, WE TOTALLY FORGOT ABOUT **PRANK DAY**!

OH **NO**!

I HAD SO MANY GREAT PRANKS PLANNED!

TOO LATE NOW. SCHOOL'S OVER.

ARRGH! WHAT WERE WE **THINKING**?

HEY, **HERE'S** AN IDEA!

WE'LL SPEND ALL SUMMER PLANNING SOME **AWESOME** PRANKS FOR THE FIRST DAY OF SCHOOL IN SEPTEMBER!

YESS! LET'S DO IT!

SHAKE ON IT!

BZZZZZZ

YANK!

FOOOSH

HI, WE'RE HERE FOR THE JUNIOR LIFE-SAVING CLASS.

THAT WAY.

RACK POOL

STAFF

I CAN'T BELIEVE MY PARENTS ARE MAKING ME DO THIS.

MAYBE IT WON'T BE SO BAD, TEDDY!

MAYBE OUR INSTRUCTOR WILL BE A TURBO HOTTIE WHO'S, LIKE, HALF LIFEGUARD, HALF **SUPERMODEL!**

AWRIGHT, SCRUBS, GET READY TO **SAVE SOME LIVES!**

COACH JOHN!

Peirce

SOME OF YOU MIGHT BE WONDERING WHY YOU'RE HERE! WELL, I'LL **TELL** YOU WHY YOU'RE HERE!

YOU'RE HERE BECAUSE WHEN YOU GO TO A **POOL PARTY** AND LITTLE JOHNNY FALLS INTO THE **DEEP END**, YOU CAN JUMP IN AND **FISH HIM OUT!**

...INSTEAD OF SITTING THERE IN A **LOUNGE CHAIR**, STUFFING YOUR FACE WITH **CHEEZ DOODLES!**

IS IT REALLY NECESSARY TO SLANDER A LEGENDARY SNACK FOOD?

POOL PARTY? THE ONLY POOLS IN **OUR** NEIGHBORHOOD ARE **INFLATABLE!**

PUT THESE ON, THEN GET IN THE WATER.

HUH? WHY ARE WE PUTTING ON CLOTHES FROM THE LOST & FOUND?

BECAUSE IF YOU FALL OFF A **BOAT**, YOU HAVE TO BE ABLE TO **INFLATE** YOUR CLOTHES TO KEEP YOURSELF **AFLOAT**!

WHA-?... THIS IS A **YANKEES** SHIRT! I'M A **RED SOX** FAN! I CAN'T WEAR **THIS**!

I'D RATHER DROWN.

TRADE YA.

ARTUR! WANNA PLAY KICK THE CAN?

KICK THE CAN? HOKAY!

WHERE I SHOULD KICK IT?

YOU CAN'T KICK IT **YET**, ARTUR!

OF **COURSE**! BECAUSE I DO NOT KNOW WHERE IS THE **GOAL**!

NO, NO... THERE ARE NO GOALS IN KICK THE CAN!

THERE'S LIKE A HOME BASE, AND...

AH! HOME BASE! SO IS LIKE **BASEBALL**!

NO, IT'S **NOT**! ONE PERSON IS IT, SEE...

WHAT "IT" IS?

THAT'S THE PERSON WHO HAS TO **FIND** EVERYBODY!

OH **HO**! I CAN FIND EVERYBODY! THEY ARE OVER **THERE**!

I AM **GOOD** AT THIS GAME!

CLANNG!!

Peirce

OKAY, KID, INTO THE WATER. I'LL PRETEND TO BE DROWNING, AND YOU PULL ME TO SHORE.

UH... OKAY, I'LL TRY.

YOU'LL **TRY**? LISTEN, CHAMP, IF YOU WANT TO BE A JUNIOR LIFESAVER, YOU CAN'T JUST **TRY!** YOU'VE GOT TO **DO!**

AND BESIDES, IT WON'T BE AS TOUGH TO RESCUE ME AS YOU THINK.

FOR SOME REASON, I'M UNUSUALLY BUOYANT.

THANKS A **LOT**, TEDDY! YOU SKIP JUNIOR LIFESAVING, AND I GET STUCK WITH **COACH JOHN** AS MY PARTNER!

I WAS TRYING TO DO A WATER RESCUE, AND I ACCIDENT- ALLY PULLED HIS **TOUPEE** OFF!

WAIT. COACH JOHN WEARS A **TOUPEE**?

CHAD, CHAD, CHAD.

MY UNCLE PEDRO CALLS HIS A "HAIR RE- STORATION SYSTEM."

THIS IS WHERE THE BOOK CLUB MEETING IS? THE **LIBRARY**?

WELL, WHAT'D YOU **EXPECT**?

I WAS HOPING IT WOULD BE IN SOME LITTLE **COFFEE SHOP** OR SOMETHING!

...OR EVEN **OUTSIDE**!

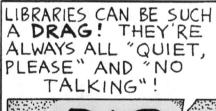

LIBRARIES CAN BE SUCH A **DRAG**! THEY'RE ALWAYS ALL "QUIET, PLEASE" AND "NO TALKING"!

PLUS, THEY'RE ALWAYS TRYING TO GET YOU TO **READ**!

YEAH, THEY'RE SO **PUSHY**!

HELLO, FRANCIS!

HI, MRS. KILEY! I BROUGHT MY FRIENDS NATE AND TEDDY!

KIDS BOOK CLUB TODAY

HELLO, BOYS! WILL YOU BE JOINING US IN THE BOOK CLUB FROM NOW ON?

UH... THAT DEPENDS ON WHAT HAPPENS NEXT WEEK.

WELL, WE'RE GOING TO START READING A **WONDERFUL** NOVEL ABOUT A...

I WAS TALKING ABOUT THE **SNACK** NEXT WEEK.

AH.

ANYTHING CHOCOLATE, AND I'M IN!

BUT NO WALNUTS. I HATE WALNUTS.

Peirce

SO YOU'RE SAYING THIS BAG OF CHEEZ DOODLES SHOULD LAST **TWO WEEKS**?

UH-HUH. IF YOU EAT ONE SERVING A DAY.

BUT IF YOU KEEP CHEEZ DOODLES AROUND THAT LONG, THEY GET **STALE!** THEN YOU'VE GOT TO THROW THEM **AWAY!** THAT'S **WASTEFUL!**

DO YOU WANT ME TO THROW AWAY CHEEZ DOODLES SO THAT THEY POLLUTE OUR WATER AND CLOG OUR LAND-FILLS?

SO BY EATING CHEEZ DOODLES, YOU'RE ACTUALLY HELPING THE ENVIRONMENT.

YES! **YES!** I'M AN **ECO-WARRIOR!**

OKAY, NATE, HERE'S 6.5 CHEEZ DOODLES. THAT'S ONE SERVING. MAKE IT LAST ALL DAY.

ALL DAY?

THAT'S **IMPOSSIBLE!!** I CAN'T SURVIVE ON **THIS!** I'LL **STARVE!**

SIIIGH..

IS THERE ANYTHING MORE PATHETIC THAN HALF A CHEEZ DOODLE?

I CAN THINK OF SOMETHING.

Peirce

A METAL DETECTOR? I BORROWED IT FROM MY GRANDFATHER!

HE SAYS THE BEACH IS THE BEST PLACE TO FIND COINS AND JEWELRY AND STUFF!

LIKE BURIED TREASURE! EXACTLY! I'LL JUST TURN IT ON, AND...

KLIK!

OOP! GUESS WHAT! IT'S DETECTING SOMETHING **ALREADY!**

boop boop

SO LONG, TEDDY! THE NEXT TIME YOU SEE ME, I MIGHT BE **RICH!**

boop boop boop

SORRY SORRY SORRY SORRY

EITHER THIS THING DOESN'T WORK, OR THAT LADY HAS A STEEL PLATE IN HER HEAD.

"ONE SERVING PER DAY."

I'M SUPPOSED TO LIVE ON THAT?

HA! I DON'T **THINK** SO!

Peirce

RF NARF NARF NARF NA
NARF NARF NARF NARF
RF NARF NARF NARF
NARF   NARF NA
F NARF   ARF NAR
RF NAR   F NARF NA
NARF (( )) NARF

CHEEZ DOODLE HAIKU

DAD, YOU'D NEVER MAKE ME DO ANYTHING YOU WOULDN'T BE WILLING TO DO YOURSELF, RIGHT?

UH... RIGHT.

WELL, IF **I** HAVE TO CUT BACK ON EATING CHEEZ DOODLES, **YOU** SHOULD HAVE TO CUT BACK ON **ICE CREAM!**

ME?... ✳KOFF!✳ I DON'T EAT ALL THAT MUCH ICE CREAM.

OH YEAH? LET'S EXAMINE THE RECYCLING BIN!

BUSTED.

...OR AS **I** LIKE TO CALL IT, THE "BEN & JERRY'S GRAVEYARD!

CARDBOARD

NOW, FOR A LOOK AT THE WEATHER, HERE'S CHIEF METEOROLOGIST CHIP CAVENDISH!

WAIT, **WHAT**? **WHO**?

WHO'S **THIS** YAHOO? WHERE'S WINK SUMMERS?

ON VACATION, PROBABLY.

BUT THEY JUST CALLED THIS GUY THE "CHIEF METEOROLOGIST"! **WINK** IS THE CHIEF METEOROLOGIST!

WELL, THEN, IT MUST BE SOMETHING ELSE.

SOMETHING ELSE?

...AND THE STORM CLOUDS GATHER.

THIS IS AN **OUTRAGE!** WHY IS **THIS** CLOWN DOING THE WEATHER INSTEAD OF WINK SUMMERS?

WHY DOES IT MATTER?

DAD! IT **MATTERS** BECAUSE WINK'S MY FAVORITE LOCAL TV PERSONALITY! **THIS** GUY IS A TOTAL **STIFF!**

HE CAN'T BANTER WITH THE CO-ANCHORS LIKE **WINK** CAN!

BANTER BANTER BANTER BANTER BANTER BANTER BONK! OW!

SEE?

Peirce

POOR WINK SUMMERS. HE **WAS** CHANNEL 12'S CHIEF METEOROLOGIST. NOW HE'S ONLY THE **WEEKEND** GUY. HE MUST BE SO BUMMED OUT.

BUT HE'S **STILL** GOING TO SUCK IT UP AND GIVE THE BEST FORECAST HE CAN! THE MAN HAS **PRIDE!** HE'S A **PRO!**

IT MIGHT RAIN TOMORROW... OR IT MIGHT NOT. HOW SHOULD **I** KNOW? WHO EVEN **CARES?**

BACK TO YOU, SUSAN.

THERE MAY BE A SHORT ADJUSTMENT PERIOD.

C'MON, LET'S GO. I TOLD TEDDY WE'D...

WHOA, FRANCIS! HOLD EVERYTHING!

LOOK AT **THIS**! A **CAPTAIN VOLTAGE** FIGURINE! I SAW ONE OF THESE FOR SALE AT "KLASSIC KOMIX" FOR A **HUNDRED BUCKS**!

...AND **THIS** GUY'S SELLING IT FOR **TEN**! HE DOESN'T REALIZE WHAT IT'S WORTH! HE HAS NO **CLUE**!

SEE ANYTHING YOU LIKE, BOYS?

ACT CASUAL! **ACT CASUAL**!!

FRANCIS, GIVE ME TEN DOLLARS!

WHAT? WHY DRAG **ME** INTO THIS?

BECAUSE THIS IS A **SURE THING!** WE BUY THIS FIGURINE FOR TEN BUCKS, AND SELL IT FOR A **HUNDRED!** WE'LL MAKE A HUGE PROFIT! WE'LL BE **RICH!**

ARE YOU **SURE** THAT THING IS WORTH A HUNDRED BUCKS?

POSITIVE! TRUST ME!

THAT'S WHAT YOU SAID WHEN YOU CONVINCED ME TO INVEST IN YOUR "FUDGE-ON-A-STICK" BUSINESS.

...WHICH WOULD HAVE WORKED IF NOT FOR THAT HEAT WAVE.

SUCCESS! WE NOW OWN A VINTAGE CAPTAIN VOLTAGE FIGURINE! WHAT AN INVESTMENT!

SO **NOW** WHAT DO WE DO?

YARD SALE
TODAY
10 - 3

WE TAKE IT DOWN TO KLASSIC KOMIX AND **SELL** IT! FOR A **HUNDRED SMACKERS!**

THEN WE JUST SIT BACK AND LIVE OFF OUR PROFITS!

LIVE OFF $45 EACH?

NO, NO, WE USE THE $45 TO BUY **STOCK!**

HEY, CHUCKLES! WHY THE LONG FACE?

HMMPH.

HMMPH WHAT?

READ THIS QUOTE.

"A CARTOONIST NEEDS TO BE A GOOD ARTIST, NOT A GREAT ARTIST, AND A GOOD WRITER, NOT A GREAT WRITER."

OKAY, SO?

SO... **I** WANT TO BE A CARTOONIST!

...BUT I'M A GREAT ARTIST! **AND** A GREAT WRITER!

I'M OVER-QUALIFIED.

RIGHT.

NOW I'LL HAVE TO SETTLE FOR BEING **PRESIDENT** OR SOME-THING!

GORDIE, MY MAN!

HI, NATE! HERE FOR THE NEW ISSUE OF "FEMME FATALITY"?

NOPE! FRANCIS AND I ARE HERE TO **CASH IN!**

SEE THIS CAPTAIN VOLTAGE FIGURINE? GUESS HOW MUCH WE PAID FOR IT AT A YARD SALE!

TEN BUCKS?

NOPE! **TEN BU—...** WAIT, WHAT?

Peirce

NATE, I'M NOT GOING TO JUST **HAND** YOU TEN DOLLARS SO YOU CAN MAKE YOUR MISTAKE MAGICALLY **DISAPPEAR**!

YOU BORROWED MONEY FROM FRANCIS TO BUY THAT THING, SO **YOU** NEED TO EARN THE MONEY TO PAY HIM BACK!

OKAY, OKAY...

YOU'RE RIGHT, DAD. THIS IS A LIFE LESSON, AND I'VE GOT TO LEARN FROM IT!

LATER...

...AND THAT'S THE **ORIGINAL PAINT**!

WOW!

POTENTIALLY PRICELESS FIGURINE $15

peirce

SPITSY, IT'S TIME FOR A LITTLE TALK.

Z

YOU'RE AFRAID OF SQUIRRELS, YOU PLAY WITH CATS, YOU WEAR A WUSSY SWEATER AND A COLLAR THAT LOOKS LIKE A SATELLITE DISH...

WAG WAG WAG WAG

BASICALLY, YOU'RE A DISGRACE TO DOGS EVERYWHERE.

BUT I HAVE A **PLAN**!

WURF!

I'M GOING TO TEACH YOU HOW TO PLAY FRISBEE! THEN AT LEAST YOU'LL HAVE **ONE** SKILL THAT'S "DOGGY"!

READY? HERE WE GO! YOU KNOW WHAT TO DO, RIGHT?

NAB!

ZING!

BONK!

OW!

? ✦ ☆ ?

GOOD DOG!

111

A 3-day weekend's
Quite a treat
For working men
And women.

That extra day
Means time to play,
Camp out, or
Have fun swimmin'.

For three full days
Of R & R,
You neither rush
Nor race.

And then the fourth
Day comes along
And smacks you
In the face.

UH... YEAH, OKAY.

HMPH.

WHAT'S THE MATTER?

WHEN THE DETENTION MONITOR SAYS "SEE YOU THIS AFTERNOON" ON THE FIRST DAY OF SCHOOL, YOU KNOW WHERE YOU STAND.

Peirce

MRS. GODFREY, I HAVE A SEATING CHART QUESTION.

HOW COME YOU MAKE US SIT IN A BOY-GIRL-BOY-GIRL PATTERN?

NATE, SURELY YOU'RE MATURE ENOUGH THAT YOU DON'T OBJECT TO SITTING NEAR GIRLS.

GIRLS? NO.

Peirce

GIRL. SINGULAR.

MRS. GODFREY, CAN I GET EXTRA CREDIT FOR FINISHING THE WORKSHEET FIRST?

MR. ROSA, MY GOAL IN ART THIS YEAR IS TO CREATE A **MASTERPIECE**!

AN ENDURING WORK OF CREATIVE GENIUS THAT DEFINES MY ARTISTIC **CAREER**!

WONDER-FUL!

JUST MAKE SURE, WHATEVER IT IS, THAT IT FITS INTO THE CUBBYHOLE I'VE ASSIGNED YOU!

THEY TELL YOU TO THINK OUTSIDE THE BOX, BUT THEY REALLY DON'T WANT YOU TO THINK OUTSIDE THE BOX.

WHAT'S ALL THIS?

I TOLD YOU I WAS GOING TO CREATE A MASTERPIECE!

THESE ARE MY PLANS FOR A HUGE MURAL I'M GOING TO PAINT! THE THEME IS "GREAT FIGURES IN WORLD HISTORY"!

THAT'S A LOT TO FIT IN A MURAL!

I KNOW. I'M HAVING TROUBLE FIGURING OUT WHO'S IN AND WHO'S OUT.

DWAYNE "THE ROCK" JOHNSON MAY END UP ON THE CUTTING ROOM FLOOR.

WELL, THERE'S A FIRST TIME FOR EVERYTHING.

NATE, I SPOKE TO THE SCHOOL IMPROVEMENT COMMITTEE ABOUT YOUR MURAL PROPOSAL.

YES! SO CAN I GET STARTED?

NOT JUST YET. FIRST THE COMMITTEE WILL RECOMMEND SEVERAL CHANGES TO THE LIST OF HISTORICAL FIGURES DEPICTED.

...AND INSTEAD OF ALLOWING YOU TO PAINT IT ALL BY YOUR**SELF**, WE'RE GOING TO INVOLVE **ALL** THE STUDENTS!

...BUT OTHER THAN **THAT**, THEY **LOVE** THE IDEA!

OH, AND IT WON'T EX- ACTLY BE A MURAL!

Peirce

YOU LOOK UPSET, NATE.

PRINCIPAL NICHOLS TOTALLY **RUINED** MY IDEA!

MY PLAN WAS: **I** PAINT A GIANT MURAL IN THE CAFETORIUM THAT WILL LAST FOR YEARS!... DECADES!... **FOREVER!**

HIS PLAN IS: **ALL** THE KIDS IN THE SCHOOL MAKE INDIVIDUAL PAINTINGS ON PIECES OF **POSTER-BOARD!**

POSTERBOARD ISN'T FOREVER.

THIS IS BARELY A STEP UP FROM PIPE-CLEANER SCULPTURE.

GOOD WIN, BOYS! GOOD WIN!

EXCEPT FOR THAT GOAL I LET IN.

IT FAKED ME OUT BECAUSE IT PICKED UP SPEED AS IT CAME AT ME.

THAT'S IMPOSSIBLE.

A BALL CAN'T ACCELER-ATE ALL BY It**SELF**! ACCORDING TO THE LAWS OF PHYSICS, IT STARTS TO **DE**CELERATE AS SOON AS IT'S KICKED!

THAT SHOT DIDN'T SPEED UP! IT JUST SLOWED DOWN LESS RAPIDLY THAN YOU **THOUGHT** IT WOULD!

SO IF I THROW THIS BALL...

... IT WILL START DECELERATING IMMEDIATELY.

DOOF!

WOW, YOU'RE **RIGHT**, FRANCIS! IT CAME TO A COMPLETE **STOP**!

I'M ACCELERATING! I'M ACCELERATING!!

I'M GOING TO COUNTERACT MY BAD HOROSCOPE WITH A BUNCH OF GOOD LUCK CHARMS! MAYBE THEN WE'LL WIN OUR GAME!

...OR **MAYBE** YOUR HOROSCOPE HAS NOTHING TO **DO** WITH OUR GAME! MAYBE HORO-SCOPES ARE JUST **RANDOM PREDICTIONS!!**

YOU'RE SUCH A PISCES.

THESE GUYS ARE A SCARY TEAM.

THEY CAN SCORE FROM ANYWHERE!

BUT I'LL BE FINE AS LONG AS I REMEMBER WHAT COACH TOLD ME:

"BE AGGRESSIVE AND STAY..." UH... WAIT, WHAT WAS THE WORD?

IT WAS A WEIRD ONE. I THINK IT BEGAN WITH A "V." HMMMMM...

VUH... VOO... VAH... VEE... VIN... VIL... V-V-V-V...

DANG! WHAT **WAS** IT?

VIVACIOUS? NO. VIGOROUS? NO.

!!AH! **GOT** IT! "BE AGGRESSIVE AND STAY...

...VIGILANT"!

IT'S **SORT** OF A SCHOOL PROJECT! I'M TAB-ULATING THE **Q** SCORES OF EVERYONE AT P.S. 38!

Q SCORES?

IT'S AN APPROVAL RATING SYSTEM! IF EVERYBODY KNOWS YOU AND LIKES YOU, YOUR Q SCORE IS ONE HUNDRED!

AND IF NOBODY LIKES YOU, YOUR Q SCORE IS ZERO?

IN MOST CASES.

FOR MRS. GODFREY, I FEEL IT'S MY DUTY TO EXPAND INTO NEGATIVE NUMBERS.

THAT'S VERY RESPONSIBLE OF YOU.

PRINCIPAL NICHOLS, WOULD YOU LIKE TO EXAMINE THE Q SCORES OF ALL THE TEACHERS? IT'S **VERY** INTERESTING!

AS YOU CAN SEE, **MRS. GODFREY'S** Q SCORE IS THE LOWEST! NOBODY CAN **STAND** THIS WOMAN! SHE'S AN EMBARRASSMENT TO THE SCHOOL!

THIS INFORMATION COULD COME IN HANDY THE NEXT TIME YOU'RE DOING HIRINGS AND...✳AHEM!✳... **FIRINGS,** IF YOU GET MY DRIFT!

WINKA WINKA WINKA

YOU'RE AN UNUSUAL BOY.

NO NEED TO THANK ME, BIG FELLA! I'M HERE TO **SERVE!**

SCHOOL PICTURE GUY!

IN THE FLESH, KID! IN THE FLESH!

I HAVE A FREE PERIOD. CAN I HANG OUT WITH YOU?

A TOP-NOTCH IDEA, CHUM! I COULD USE THE HELP!

I'VE GOT A CLASS OF FIRST-GRADERS UP NEXT, AND THEY CAN BE A BIT OF A HANDFUL!

I THINK I'M ABOUT TO THROW UP.

OKAY, CHAMP, SHOW TIME.

NO OFFENSE, SCHOOL PICTURE GUY, BUT A LOT OF THE SHOTS FROM THAT LAST SESSION AREN'T SO GREAT.

UH-HUH.

MOST OF THESE KIDS AREN'T EVEN **SMILING**.

RIGHT.

...AND **HALF** OF 'EM HAVE THEIR **EYES** CLOSED!

EXACTLY.

YOU'RE TAKING LOUSY PICTURES ON **PURPOSE!**

SSSH!

...AND WHAT WAS THE NAME OF HAMILTON'S OPPONENT?...

...NATE.

ME?

UMMM...

OOH!

WHAT'S YOUR **PROBLEM**, GINA?

I'M RAISING MY HAND!

ExCUSE ME, BUT **I'M** ANSWERING THE QUESTION!

⁂SNORT!⁂ RIGHT. LIKE **YOU** KNOW THE ANSWER!

OH, **YEAH**? WHAT MAKES YOU SO SURE I **DON'T**?

TAP TAP

I HAPPEN TO BE THINKING OF THE ANSWER THIS VERY **MINUTE**!

YAWNNN...

...AND THE ANSWER IIIIIIIS...

...I.M. GASSY!

HA HA HA HA HA HA HA HA HA HA HA HA HA HA HA

YOU'RE A RIOT.

I THINK JENNY IS TOO YOUNG TO HAVE A STEADY BOYFRIEND.

SNORT! UNLESS **YOU** WERE HER BOYFRIEND! **THEN** SHE WOULDN'T BE TOO YOUNG!

WHY WOULD IT BE OKAY FOR JENNY TO DATE **YOU**, BUT IT'S **NOT** OKAY FOR HER TO DATE **ARTUR**?

BECAUSE I'M ME.

RIGHT. I FORGOT.

WELL, COME **ON**, FRANCIS! **THINK!**

Peirce

IT JUST DOESN'T ADD UP.

WHAT DOESN'T?

WHY JENNY PREFERS **ARTUR** TO **ME**! HERE'S THE ARTUR COLUMN, AND HERE'S THE NATE COLUMN!

HE'S GOOD AT MATH, SCIENCE AND MAKING THE HONOR ROLL. **I'M** GOOD AT SPORTS, CARTOONING, AND BEING SMOLDERINGLY CHARISMATIC.

ADVANTAGE, MOI.

BY A LANDSLIDE.

I THINK I KNOW WHY JENNY LIKES ARTUR BETTER THAN ME!

DO TELL.

IT'S THE GOOFY WAY HE **TALKS!** FOR SOME REASON, EVERYBODY THINKS HIS FRACTURED ENGLISH IS **CHARMING!**

SO ALL I HAVE TO DO TO WIN JENNY'S HEART IS START TALKING IN STUPID-SOUNDING **GIBBERISH!**

"START"?

WHEN DOES THE CHARMING PART KICK IN?

STILL TRYING TO BREAK UP JENNY AND ARTUR?

I'M **NOT** TRYING TO BREAK THEM UP, FRANCIS!

I'M JUST SHOWING JENNY THAT I HAVE A LOT TO OFFER!... THAT I'M PRIME BOYFRIEND MATERIAL!

MAYBE SHE'LL READ THIS AND REALIZE THAT I'M HER **SOUL MATE**!

FYI, "ARTUR" AND "MANURE" DON'T REALLY RHYME.

EX**CUSE** ME, IT'S **FREE VERSE**!

LOOK, MRS. GODFREY! "NO LOUD VOICES"! IT'S ONE OF YOUR **CLASSROOM RULES!**

NO LOUD VOICES

SO HOW COME YOU LET GINA SCREAM "OOH" AT THE TOP OF HER LUNGS WHEN-EVER SHE RAISES HER HAND?

BECAUSE, NATE, WHEN A STUDENT FEELS PASSIONATELY ABOUT SOMETHING, IT'S MY JOB TO BE **EN**COURAGING, NOT **DIS**-COURAGING.

NOW SIT DOWN AND PUT YOUR HEAD ON YOUR DESK.

GREAT

Peirce

IT'S SO **OBVIOUS** THAT **GINA** IS MRS. GODFREY'S **FAVORITE**! I THOUGHT TEACHERS WERE SUPPOSED TO TREAT EVERYONE THE **SAME**!

WELL, IF YOU OWNED TWO CATS, AND ONE OF THEM WAS WELL-BEHAVED AND THE OTHER WAS ALWAYS SCRATCHING THE FURNITURE, WHICH WOULD **YOU** PREFER?

KNOW WHAT I MEAN?

I WOULD **NEVER** OWN A CAT.

HE DOESN'T KNOW WHAT I MEAN.

MR. ROSA, TEACHERS AREN'T SUPPOSED TO PLAY FAVORITES, RIGHT?

WELL, **MRS. GODFREY** DOES! **GINA'S** HER FAVORITE! IT'S SO **ANNOYING!**

NATE, YOU KNOW I CAN'T DISCUSS MRS. GODFREY WITH YOU.

YEAH...

SO LET'S DISCUSS **GINA**, THEN! SHE IS SUCH A...

STOP.

YOU'RE RIGHT, NATE. TEACHERS AREN'T SUPPOSED TO HAVE FAVORITE STUDENTS.

BUT?...

BUT WHAT?

BUT THEY **DO**! ALL TEACHERS HAVE FAVORITES DEEP DOWN! IT'S SO **OBVIOUS**!

I MEAN, IT'S COMMON KNOWLEDGE THAT I'M **YOUR** PERSONAL FAVORITE!

IT IS?

YEAH, BUT I DON'T FLAUNT IT. I KEEP IT ON THE DOWN-LOW.

DAD, CAN I GO TRICK-OR-TREATING IN TEDDY'S NEIGHBORHOOD THIS YEAR?

WHAT'S WRONG WITH **OUR** NEIGHBORHOOD?

IT'S **BORING**! EVERYBODY HANDS OUT THE SAME STUFF!

I DON'T!

I ALWAYS TRY TO PROVIDE A TREAT THAT'S... THAT'S...

I BELIEVE THE WORD IS "INAPPROPRIATE."

THIS YEAR: TOFU KABOBS!

HOWDY, BOYS!

WHERE'VE YOU **BEEN?** WE ALMOST STARTED WITHOUT YOU!

SORRY. MY DAD MADE RICE KRISPIE TREATS TO HAND OUT, AND I HAD TO HELP HIM PUT THEM IN LITTLE BAGGIES.

...WHICH REMINDS ME, HE SENT THESE ALONG FOR YOU GUYS.

THEY... UH... LOOK A LITTLE WEIRD.

WE WERE OUT OF RICE KRISPIES, SO HE USED ACTUAL RICE.

172

ISBN 978-1-338-03326-7

12 11 10 9 8 7 6 5 4 3 2 1   16 17 18 19 20 21

Printed in the U.S.A.   40

First Scholastic printing, January 2016

These strips appeared in newspapers from May 15, 2011,
through October 30, 2011.